"Many Christians are forgiven but ... is a great course for helping people ... e Father wants for us."
Mark Stibbe

Saint Andrew's Church, Chorleywood

"Freedom in Christ Ministries has given us tools to help establish individuals as secure, whole people in Christ. This is not something that will come and go like a spiritual fashion."
John Groves

Winchester Family Church

"Such spiritual common sense... What a great way to start discipleship."
Gerald Coates

Pioneer

"We are excited about The Freedom In Christ Discipleship Course. It enables Christians to face the issues from their past and find a pathway to wholeness. I can highly recommend this material for use within the Cell movement."
Laurence Singlehurst

Cell UK

"The Freedom in Christ Discipleship Course is Bible-based, Christ-centred and non-condemnatory. It is not a quick fix but leads people into a permanent solution. There is a breath of fresh air about this down-to-earth, God-inspired approach."
Ben Davies

Bracknell Family Church

"Using FIC teaching and principles, we've seen many Christians' lives transformed. The whole church is stronger and more unified as a result. I highly recommend it to other leaders."
Rod Woods

The City Temple, London

Comments from people who have used this material

"I have a clear head, praise Jesus — it's not been really clear for years!"

"Knowing who I am in Christ and accepting the truth of God while rejecting the lies of the devil has changed my life."

"It is helping me to grow and mature as a Christian as never before."

"My life has been transformed. It truly was like walking from darkness back into light again."

"I was separated from the truth of God's love and Jesus' liberation by a large wall of pain, wounds and lies. But the wall came tumbling down."

"It proved to be a pivotal point in my Christian life... I now feel that I have the abundant life which Christ spoke of and which I have been yearning for."

The Freedom in Christ

Discipleship Course

Participant's Workbook

Neil T. Anderson and Steve Goss

MONARCH
BOOKS

Oxford, UK

Published in the UK in 2004 by Monarch Books
(a publishing imprint of Lion Hudson plc),
Mayfield House, 256 Banbury Road, Oxford OX2 7DH.
Tel: +44 (0) 1865 302750 Fax: +44 (0) 1865 302757
Email: monarch@lionhudson.com
www.lionhudson.com

Illustrations by Beverley Hutton and Helen Mair

UK ISBN 1 85424 654 2
(pack of 5) 1 85424 655 0

Distributed in the UK by Marston Book Services Ltd.,
PO Box 269, Abingdon, Oxon OX14 4YN.

British Library Cataloguing Data
A catalogue record for this book is available
from the British Library.

Designed and produced for the publishers by:
Robell Design, PO Box 2016, Reading RG2 9SZ
and
Lion Hudson plc.

Printed in England

Contents

Part A — Key Truths

Jesus said that we will know the truth and the truth will set us free! In the first three sessions we look at some of the key truths we need to know about what it means to be a Christian.

Part B — The World, The Flesh And The Devil

Every day the world, the flesh and the devil conspire to push us away from truth. Understanding how they work will enable us to stand firm.

Part C — Breaking The Hold Of The Past

God does not change our past but by His grace He enables us to walk free of it. This section includes going through The Steps To Freedom In Christ (see separate booklet *The Steps To Freedom In Christ*).

Part D — Growing As Disciples

Having taken hold of our freedom in Christ, we now want to grow to maturity. In this section we will learn how to stand firm, how to relate to other people and how to stay on the path of becoming more like Jesus.

Why Take Part In This Course?

- **Break through to spiritual maturity and bear fruit**
- **Uncover areas of deception**
- **Resolve personal and spiritual conflicts**
- **Break free from negative thinking**

Through His victory on the cross over sin, death and the devil, Christ has set us free. But sometimes it doesn't feel like it! Many sense that they have not reached their full potential. Perhaps they feel "stuck" in habitual sin, negative thoughts, fears, unforgiveness or condemnation. Maybe they are bogged down by "the cares of life". Yet they really want to grow and mature.

The good news is that when Jesus said that the truth would set us free, He meant it! This course will help you grasp the amazing truth of your new identity in Christ, teach you to uncover and resist the enemy's deception, and help you move on. It's not a "quick fix". But it is likely to revolutionise your Christian life. No matter how long or short a time it is since you became a Christian, you will benefit from this course.

How Can I Get The Most Out Of It?

Do your best to get to each session.

Read *Victory Over The Darkness* and *The Bondage Breaker* by Neil Anderson to reinforce the teaching on the course.

Use the suggestions for your quiet times at the end of each session and consider the "big question".

Ensure you go through The Steps To Freedom In Christ, a kind and gentle process during which you ask the Holy Spirit to show you any areas of your life where you may need to repent. Most churches schedule this between Sessions 9 and 10 and for many it is a life-changing experience.

Make it part of your daily life. The course includes strategies for standing firm in the freedom won and renewing your mind on an ongoing basis. Those who do this benefit the most.

Session 1
Where Did I Come From?

Focus Verse

1 John 5:12: He who has the Son has life; he who does not have the Son does not have life.

Objective

To understand how Adam and Eve's disobedience led to our being born spiritually dead with driving needs for significance, security and acceptance.

Welcome

Spend a couple of minutes in pairs finding out as much as you can about each other. Then, in no more than 30 seconds, answer this question about your partner: "Who is he/she?"

Or: What would it take to make you really happy in life?

Worship

Suggested theme: God's eternal plans and how He always fulfils them. See Isaiah 46:10, Philippians 1:1-6.

Word
Who Are You Really?

What makes up the real "me"? Is it my body? Is it what I have? Is it what I do? Is it what I think?

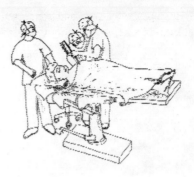

We Are Created In The Image Of God

God is Spirit and we too have a spiritual nature, an inner person (or soul). It is not our outer person that is created in the image of God; it's our inner person that has the capacity to think, feel and choose.

How We Were Designed To Be

Physically Alive
Our spirit connected to our body

Spiritually Alive
Our spirit connected to God

Being spiritually alive and connected to God meant that Adam and Eve possessed a number of very important qualities of life:

1. Significance

2. Security

3. Acceptance

Pause for Thought 1
Imagine Adam and Eve's daily life as they were originally created. How would it have been different from yours? What do you think they thought about as they dropped off to sleep each night?

The Consequence Of The Fall
Spiritual Death

The effects of Adam and Eve's sin can be summed up by one word: "death". Some of the effects of this spiritual death for them (and consequently for us) were:

1. Lost knowledge of God
"They are darkened in their understanding and separated from the life of God because of the ignorance that is in them due to the hardening of their hearts" (Ephesians 4:18).

2. Negative emotions

a. They felt fearful and anxious

b. They felt guilty and shameful

c. They felt rejected

d. They felt weak and powerless

e. They felt depressed and angry

Pause for Thought 2
Do you recall becoming aware of these feelings of guilt, powerlessness and rejection? Which do you particularly identify with?

Trying To Go Back To How It Was Meant To Be

The best the world can offer does not work

The world offers us a number of false equations which it promises will recover what Adam and Eve lost:

> Performance + accomplishments = significance
> Status + recognition = security
> Appearance + admiration = acceptance

"Utterly meaningless! Everything is meaningless." (Ecclesiastes 1:2)

Obeying rules does not work

What Jesus Came To Do
Give Us Back Spiritual Life

"In the beginning was the Word... In him was *life*, and that *life* was the light of men" (John 1:1-4). (Our emphasis)

"I have come that they may have *life*, and have it to the full" (John 10:10). (Our emphasis)

"I am the resurrection and the *life*. He who believes in me will live, even though he dies" (John 11:25). (Our emphasis)

What Adam lost was *life*. What Jesus came to give us was *life*.

Restore Significance, Security And Acceptance

Did you think that eternal life is something that you get when you die? It's much more than that — it's a whole different quality of life right now. "He who has the Son has life; he who does not have the Son does not have life" (1 John 5:12).

Pause for Thought 3
Not all of the things on the list we have just read will feel true. If God says something about you, is it true even if it doesn't feel true?

Significance, Security & Acceptance Restored In Christ

I Am Significant

I am no longer worthless, inadequate, helpless or hopeless. In Christ I am deeply significant and special. God says:

Matthew 5:13,14	I am the salt of the earth and the light of the world.
John 15:1,5	I am a branch of the true vine, Jesus, a channel of His life.
John 15:16	I have been chosen and appointed by God to bear fruit.
Acts 1:8	I am a personal, Spirit-empowered witness of Christ.
1 Corinthians 3:16	I am a temple of God.
2 Corinthians 5:17-21	I am a minister of reconciliation for God.
2 Corinthians 6:1	I am God's fellow worker.
Ephesians 2:6	I am seated with Christ in the heavenly realms.
Ephesians 2:10	I am God's workmanship, created for good works.
Ephesians 3:12	I may approach God with freedom and confidence.
Philippians 4:13	I can do all things through Christ who strengthens me!

I Am Secure

I am no longer guilty, unprotected, alone or abandoned. In Christ I am totally secure. God says:

Romans 8:1,2	I am free forever from condemnation.
Romans 8:28	I am assured that all things work together for good.
Romans 8:31-34	I am free from any condemning charges against me.
Romans 8:35-39	I cannot be separated from the love of God.
2 Corinthians 1:21,22	I have been established, anointed and sealed by God.
Philippians 1:6	I am confident that the good work God has begun in me will be perfected.
Philippians 3:20	I am a citizen of heaven.
Colossians 3:3	I am hidden with Christ in God.
2 Timothy 1:7	I have not been given a spirit of fear, but of power, love and a sound mind.
Hebrews 4:16	I can find grace and mercy to help in time of need.
1 John 5:18	I am born of God and the evil one cannot touch me.

I Am Accepted

I am no longer rejected, unloved or dirty. In Christ I am completely accepted. God says:

John 1:12	I am God's child.
John 15:15	I am Christ's friend.
Romans 5:1	I have been justified.
1 Corinthians 6:17	I am united with the Lord and I am one spirit with Him.
1 Corinthians 6:19,20	I have been bought with a price. I belong to God.
1 Corinthians 12:27	I am a member of Christ's Body.
Ephesians 1:1	I am a saint, a holy one.
Ephesians 1:5	I have been adopted as God's child.
Ephesians 2:18	I have direct access to God through the Holy Spirit.
Colossians 1:14	I have been redeemed and forgiven for all my sins.
Colossians 2:10	I am complete in Christ.

Witness

How do people generally try to deal with their strong need to feel accepted, significant and secure? How would you explain to a non-Christian neighbour that ultimately these are found only in Christ?

Questions For Groups

1. Imagine Adam and Eve's daily life as they were originally created. How would it have been different from yours? What do you think they thought about as they dropped off to sleep each night?

2. What was the main effect of Adam's sin on us?

3. What was the effect on our emotions? Do you recall becoming aware of feelings of guilt, powerlessness and rejection? Which do you particularly identify with?

4. What did Jesus come to do about this? What fundamentally did He come to give us?

5. We read together a list of things that God says about us if we are alive "in Christ" (see pages 12-13). Do all of those things feel true to you?

6. If God says something about you, is it true even if it doesn't feel true?

To Take Away

Suggestions For Your Quiet Times This Week:

Read the Significance, Security & Acceptance Restored In Christ list out loud every day. Then pick one of the truths that is particularly relevant to you and spend some time reading it in its context and asking the Lord to help you understand it more fully.

Big Question (to consider before the next session):

Imagine you are talking to a not-yet Christian. Can you summarise the gospel message in a few sentences? There will be an opportunity to share what you have written at the next session if you want to.

Session 2
Who Am I Now?

Focus Verse

2 Corinthians 5:17: If anyone is in Christ, he is a new creation; the old has gone, the new has come.

Objective

To realise that deep down inside we are now completely new creations in Christ.

Focus Truth

Your decision to follow Christ was the defining moment of your life and led to a complete change in who you are.

Welcome

Imagine you are talking to a not-yet Christian. Can you summarise the gospel message in a sentence or two?

Or: How was the gospel message explained to you when you became a Christian?

Worship

Suggested theme: God loves us and even delights in us, even though we don't deserve it. See Ephesians 2:4,5, Luke 15:17-24, Romans 5:10,11.

Word

Who Am I Now?

At one time, "we were by nature objects of wrath" (Ephesians 2:3). Everything changed when you became a Christian:

"If anyone is in Christ, he is a new creation; the old has gone, the new has come!" (2 Corinthians 5:17)

"For you were once darkness, but now you are light in the Lord." (Ephesians 5:8)

"He has rescued us from the dominion of darkness and brought us into the kingdom of the Son he loves." (Colossians 1:13)

A Saint — Not A Sinner

"While we were still sinners, Christ died for us" (Romans 5:8).

Even the youngest Christian is a "saint".

We are saints because of our new identity and position "in Christ".

Pause For Thought 1
Look again at the Significance, Security & Acceptance Restored In Christ list from the last session. Which of those is particularly significant to you?
Do you find it difficult to believe that those things really apply to you?
If God has said they are true of you, are they true?

Not Just Forgiven But A Whole New Person

Changed Behaviour Comes From Realising You Are A Whole New Person

If you think of yourself as a forgiven sinner (but still a sinner), what are you likely to do? Sin! If you want to change your behaviour you have to see yourself as more than just forgiven.

If you came across a dead man and you wanted to save him you would have to:
1. Work out how to cure the disease that caused him to die (in our case, sin).
2. Give him life again.

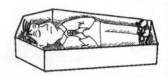

If we knew only the truth that Jesus died to cure the problem of sin, we would believe that we were forgiven sinners. Knowing the truth that we have also received back the life that Adam lost and become saints is crucial if we want to live a life that honours God.

Defeat Comes From *Not* Realising You Are A Whole New Person

Satan can't do anything to change that historical fact of who you now are but if he can get you to believe a lie about who you are, he can cripple your walk with the Lord.

You are not saved by how you *behave* but by how you *believe*.

Being Pleasing To God

What Happens When I Go Wrong?

The problem we have with seeing ourselves as saints rather than sinners is that we are painfully aware that we do sometimes sin.

It's Not Inevitable — But We Do Sometimes Go Wrong
"If we claim to be without sin, we deceive ourselves and the truth is not in us" (1 John 1:8).

You are not a sinner in the hands of an angry God. You are a saint in the hands of a loving God.

Our Fundamental Relationship With Our Heavenly Father Does Not Change When We Sin

"My dear children, I write this to you so that you will not sin. But if anybody does sin, we have one who speaks to the Father in our defence — Jesus Christ, the Righteous One" (1 John 2:1).

We Restore Harmony By Turning Back To Him And Away From Our Sin

A harmonious relationship is based on trust and obedience — when either is lacking it affects the quality of the relationship.

God Does Not Condemn Us

"Therefore, there is now no condemnation for those who are in Christ Jesus." (Romans 8:1)

Pause For Thought 2
Imagine that you have fallen for a lie of the enemy and done something that you know is very wrong. What is an appropriate way to behave at that point? What can you do if you feel really condemned?

We Don't Have To Try To Become What We Already Are

What can I do to be accepted by God? Nothing at all. Because you are already accepted by God simply because of what Christ has done!

It is not what we *do* that determines who we *are*. It's who we *are* that determines what we *do*.

Witness

If you were asked by a neighbour to explain the difference between a Christian and someone who is not yet a Christian, what would you say? Do you think that a Christian is in any way better than a non-Christian? What would you say to someone who asks you, "Why should I become a Christian?"

Questions For Groups

1. Has this session helped your understanding of what happened the moment you became a Christian? (See 2 Corinthians 5:17; Ephesians 5:8; Colossians 1:13). Put into your own words what happened.

2. Do you still see yourself as "a sinner saved by grace"?

3. Given that Christians still clearly do sin, do you think it is just playing with words to say that "we are not sinners but saints" — or is there a significant truth there?

4. Why is it important to see yourself as something more than just forgiven?

5. Imagine that you have fallen for a lie of the enemy and done something that you know is very wrong. What is an appropriate way to behave at that point?

6. What can you do if, having gone wrong, you feel really condemned? (Read Romans 8:1, Hebrews 10:16-22 and 1 John 1:8-2:2 to help you understand how God views Christians who sin.)

7. What truths are particularly significant to you in the My Father God list?

8. Do you think that the way we tend to see God is affected by our experiences with our less-than-perfect human fathers (in other words, if we felt, for example, that we could never do enough to please our earthly father, do we feel that God is just the same — when in fact the truth is that we are already accepted by Him)?

To Take Away

Suggestions For Your Quiet Times This Week:

Read the My Father God list out loud every day. Then pick one of the truths that is particularly relevant to you and spend some time reading it in its context and asking the Lord to help you understand it more fully.

Big Question (to consider before the next session):

Do you believe that an atheist has more or less faith than a Christian? What about a Hindu or a Muslim? What about someone who "just doesn't know"?

My Father God

I renounce the lie that my Father God is:	I joyfully accept the truth that my Father God is:
distant and uninterested in me.	intimate and involved (see Psalm 139:1-18).
insensitive and uncaring.	kind and compassionate (see Psalm 103:8-14).
stern and demanding.	accepting and filled with joy and love (see Romans 15:7; Zephaniah 3:17).
passive and cold.	warm and affectionate (see Isaiah 40:11; Hosea 11:3,4).
absent or too busy for me.	always with me and eager to be with me (see Hebrews 13:5; Jeremiah 31:20; Ezekiel 34:11-16).
impatient, angry or never satisfied with what I do.	patient and slow to anger and delights in those who put their hope in His unfailing love (see Exodus 34:6; 2 Peter 3:9, Psalm 147:11).
mean, cruel or abusive.	loving and gentle and protective (see Jeremiah 31:3; Isaiah 42:3; Psalm 18:2).
trying to take all the fun out of life.	trustworthy and wants to give me a full life; His will is good, perfect and acceptable for me (see Lamentations 3:22 23; John 10:10; Romans 12:1,2).
controlling or manipulative.	full of grace and mercy, and gives me freedom to fail (see Hebrews 4:15,16; Luke 15:11-16).

I renounce the lie that my Father God is:	I joyfully accept the truth that my Father God is:
condemning or unforgiving.	tender-hearted and forgiving; His heart and arms are always open to me (see Psalm 130:1-4; Luke 15:17-24).
nit-picking or a demanding perfectionist.	committed to my growth and proud of me as His growing child (see Romans 8:28.29; Hebrews 12:5-11; 2 Corinthians 7:14).

I Am the Apple of His Eye!

Session 3
Choosing To Believe The Truth

Focus Verse

Hebrews 11:6: Without faith it is impossible to please God, because anyone who comes to him must believe that he exists and that he rewards those who earnestly seek him.

Objective

To understand that everyone lives by faith in something or someone and that faith in God is no more than finding out what is already actually true and choosing to believe and act on it.

Focus Truth

God is truth. Find out what He has said is true and choose to believe it, whether it feels true or not, and your Christian life will be transformed.

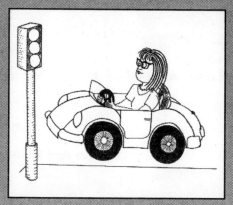

Welcome

Have you had a prayer answered recently? Share the story.
Do you believe that an atheist has more or less faith than a Christian? What about a Hindu or a Muslim? What about someone who "just doesn't know"?

Worship

Suggested theme: "awesome God". See Psalm 24; Revelation 4:8-11.

Word

Without Faith We Cannot Please God

Faith Is A Crucial Issue
We are saved through faith. Everywhere you look in the Bible you read that we are to walk by faith. A real, living faith is the key to success in your walk with the Lord.

Faith is simply believing what is already true.

Find out what is already true; choose to believe it whether it feels true or not, and your Christian life will be transformed.

Whether Faith Is Effective Depends On What Or Whom You Believe In

Everyone Lives And Operates By Faith

The issue of faith is not that we believe. Everyone believes in something or someone.

The Only Difference Between Christian And Non-Christian Faith Is What We Believe In

Jesus Christ Is The Ultimate Faith Object

Think about an occasion when you took God at His word — what happened?

Do you agree that everyone lives by faith? How much faith do you think it takes to believe that the whole universe came about by chance?

Do you agree that it's whom or what you put your faith in that determines whether it is effective? Or is it more to do with how much faith you have?

Everyone Can Grow In Faith

How Much Faith We Have Is Determined By How Well We Know The One We Put Our Faith In

"How long will you waver between two opinions? If the Lord is God, follow Him; but if Baal is God, follow him" (1 Kings 18:21). Faith is about making a choice to believe what God says is true and living our life accordingly.

You don't feel your way into good behaviour — you behave your way into good feelings.

Pause For Thought 2
*Can you think of a time when you asked God to do something
but you were disappointed because He didn't do what you
asked, or didn't do it in the way you asked? (Did you perhaps
pray faithfully for someone to get better — but they died?)
What do you conclude from such difficult experiences?*

Faith Grows In Difficult Times

Faith Leads To Action

James 2:17-18: Faith by itself, if it is not accompanied by action, is dead.
But someone will say, "You have faith: I have deeds." Show me your faith
without deeds, and I will show you my faith by what I do.

People don't always live according to what they say they believe, but they
will always live according to what they actually believe.

Pause For Thought 3
*Elijah said: "How long will you waver between two opinions?
If the Lord is God, follow Him; but if Baal is God, follow him"
(1 Kings 18:21). Will you take this opportunity to make a new
commitment to base your life completely on what God says is
true, regardless of your feelings and regardless of the
opinions of others? Spend some time in prayer telling God
what you are going to do.*

Witness

Think of someone you know who is not yet a Christian. What does the Bible say about why they don't yet believe (see 2 Corinthians 4:4; Romans 10:14-15)? Write a prayer you could pray that specifically asks God to do something about the things that are stopping them from believing. Then take God at His word and pray it!

Questions For Groups

1. Tell the group about an occasion when you took God at His word — what happened?

2. Do you agree that everyone lives by faith? How much faith do you think it takes to believe that the whole universe came about by chance?

3. Do you agree that it's whom or what you put your faith in that determines whether your faith is effective? Or is it more to do with how much faith you have?

4. Is it a new concept to you that faith is simply making a choice to believe what is already true? Did you think it was more like the little boy's view that "faith is trying hard to believe something you know isn't really true"?

5. Can you think of a time when you asked God to do something but you were disappointed because He didn't do what you asked, or didn't do it in the way you asked? (Did you perhaps pray faithfully for someone to get better – but they died?) What do you conclude from such difficult experiences?

6. Elijah said: "How long will you waver between two opinions? If the Lord is God, follow him; but if Baal is God, follow him" (1 Kings 18:21). Will you take this opportunity to make a new commitment to base your life completely on what God says is true, regardless of your feelings and regardless of the opinions of others? Spend some time in prayer with the group and tell God what you are going to do.

Twenty "Cans" of Success

1. Why should I say I can't when the Bible says I can do all things through Christ who gives me strength (Philippians 4:13)?

2. Why should I lack when I know that God shall supply all my needs according to His riches in glory in Christ Jesus (Philippians 4:19)?

3. Why should I fear when the Bible says God has not given me a spirit of fear, but one of power, love and a sound mind (2 Timothy 1:7)?

4. Why should I lack faith to fulfil my calling knowing that God has allotted to me a measure of faith (Romans 12:3)?

5. Why should I be weak when the Bible says that the Lord is the strength of my life and that I will display strength and take action because I know God (Psalm 27:1; Daniel 11:32)?

6. Why should I allow Satan supremacy over my life when He that is in me is greater than he that is in the world (1 John 4:4)?

7. Why should I accept defeat when the Bible says that God always leads me in triumph (2 Corinthians 2:14)?

8. Why should I lack wisdom when Christ became wisdom to me from God and God gives wisdom to me generously when I ask Him for it (1 Corinthians 1:30; James 1:5)?

9. Why should I be depressed when I can recall to mind God's loving kindness, compassion and faithfulness and have hope (Lamentations 3:21-23)?

10. Why should I worry and fret when I can cast all my anxiety on Christ who cares for me (1 Peter 5:7)?

11.   Why should I ever be in bondage knowing that, where the Spirit of the Lord is, there is freedom (2 Corinthians 3:17; Galatians 5:1)?

12.   Why should I feel condemned when the Bible says I am not condemned because I am in Christ (Romans 8:1)?

13.   Why should I feel alone when Jesus said He is with me always and He will never leave me nor forsake me (Matthew 28:20; Hebrews 13:5)?

14.   Why should I feel accursed or that I am the victim of bad luck when the Bible says that Christ redeemed me from the curse of the law that I might receive His Spirit (Galatians 3:13,14)?

15.   Why should I be discontented when I, like Paul, can learn to be content in all my circumstances (Philippians 4:11)?

16.   Why should I feel worthless when Christ became sin on my behalf that I might become the righteousness of God in Him (2 Corinthians 5:21)?

17.   Why should I have a persecution complex knowing that nobody can be against me when God is for me (Romans 8:31)?

18.   Why should I be confused when God is the author of peace and He gives me knowledge through His indwelling Spirit (1 Corinthians 14:33; 1 Corinthians 2:12)?

19.   Why should I feel like a failure when I am a conqueror in all things through Christ (Romans 8:37)?

20.   Why should I let the pressures of life bother me when I can take courage knowing that Jesus has overcome the world and its tribulations (John 16:33)?

To Take Away

Suggestions For Your Quiet Times This Week:
Every day read the Twenty Cans Of Success list out loud. Then pick one of the truths that is particularly appropriate to you and make a decision to believe it regardless of feelings and circumstances. If you can find a way of stepping out in faith in some practical way based on that truth, so much the better!

Big Question (to consider before the next session):
Do you think that the way you look at the world and what you believe would be very different if you had been brought up in a different culture?

Session 4
The World's View Of Truth

Focus Verse

Romans 12:2: Do not conform any longer to the pattern of this world, but be transformed by the renewing of your mind. Then you will be able to test and approve what God's will is—his good, pleasing and perfect will.

Objective

To understand that Christians need to make a definite decision to turn away from believing what the world teaches and choose instead to believe what God says is true.

Focus Truth

The world we grew up in influenced us to look at life in a particular way and to see that way as "true". However, if it doesn't stack up with what God says is true, we need to reject it and bring our beliefs into line with what really is true.

Welcome

If you could go anywhere in the world, where would you choose?

Do you think that the way you look at the world and what you believe would be very different if you had been brought up in a different culture?

Worship

Suggested theme: God is truth. Psalm 31:1-5; John 4:23-24; John 14:6-7.

Word

We All Have A "Worldview"

"A set of presuppositions or assumptions which we hold (consciously or subconsciously) about the basic make-up of the world."
James Sire (*The Universe Next Door*, Downers Grove, Ill.: InterVarsity, 1976, p.17).

Your worldview acts like a filter

Where Did Your Worldview Come From?

Past Experiences

Culture

Examples Of Different Worldviews

1. Animism: A Non-Western Worldview

Two sources of spiritual power: "mana" (neutral); good and evil spirits

Need an expert to manipulate spiritual power to your advantage

2. The Western Or "Modern" Worldview

Spiritual things are irrelevant to daily life

Reality is defined only by what we can see, touch and measure

3. The Postmodern Worldview

"There are many kinds of eyes..., and consequently there are many kinds of 'truths', and consequently there is no truth."
Friedrich Nietzsche (1844 to 1900)

There is no such thing as objective truth
Everyone has their own version of "truth"

Each person's "truth" is as valid as everyone else's

If you disagree with my "truth" or disapprove of my actions, you are rejecting *me*

Pause for Thought 1
Are you beginning to see that you have grown up with a particular worldview? How different would it be if you had grown up in another part of the world? Is your worldview more or less valid than that of someone who grew up in another part of the world? What measure would you use to judge whether someone's worldview is accurate?

The Biblical Worldview

Truth does exist

God is truth

Faith and logic are not incompatible

What happens when you die?

Hinduism teaches that when a soul dies it is reincarnated in another form.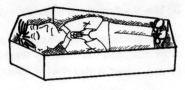

Christianity teaches that souls spend eternity in either heaven or hell.

Atheists believe that we have no soul and that when we die our existence simply ends.

Postmodernism says that you can make up whatever you want to believe as long as you don't hurt anyone else.

Logic says that we will all have the same experience regardless of what we choose to believe before the actual event.

"In the biblical view, truth is that which is ultimately, finally and absolutely real, or 'the way it is', and therefore is utterly trustworthy and dependable, being grounded and anchored in God's own reality and truthfulness."
Os Guinness (*Time For Truth*, Baker Books, 2000, p.78)

Pause For Thought 2
When we stick up for truth, how can we do so without coming across as arrogant? If we disagree with someone's beliefs or actions, does it mean that we are at the same time rejecting them as a person?

Beware Of Mix 'n' Match

We say we believe the Bible, but are many of our decisions made on the basis of what we can afford rather than on what God is saying?
We say we believe in the power of prayer, but does the way we spend our time bear this out?

Which of these best describes why you are a Christian?

❏ I believe because Christianity seems to work
❏ What I have experienced leads me to feel that Christianity is true
❏ I believe that Jesus Christ is the only way to God for all people everywhere at all times
❏ I have simply made a decision that Christianity is true for me

"The Christian faith is not true because it works; it works because it is true... It is not simply 'true for us'; it is true for any who seek in order to find, because truth is true even if nobody believes it and falsehood is false even if everybody believes it." (Os Guinness, *Time For Truth*, Baker Books, 2000, pages 79-80)

"Don't Let The World Squeeze You Into Its Mould"

Christian faith is "choosing to believe what God says is true" because we have made a decision that the biblical worldview is how things really are.

Repentance literally means a change of mind. When we repent we make a radical decision to renounce the lies of this world and choose "the way, the truth and the life". For a Christian to do less is to be "a double-minded man, unstable in all he does" (James 1:8).

Witness

How will understanding that we all grow up with a particular way of looking at the world help you as you talk to people who are not yet Christians? What will you say to those with a postmodern worldview who regard strong beliefs as a negative thing?

Questions For Groups

1. Are you beginning to see that you have grown up with a particular worldview? Which of the three views we looked at best corresponds to the one you grew up with?

2. How different would it be if you had grown up in another part of the world?

3. Is your worldview more or less valid than that of someone who grew up in another part of the world?

4. What measure would you use to judge whether someone's worldview is true?

5. When we stick up for what we believe to be the truth, how can we do so without coming across as arrogant?

6. If we disagree with someone's beliefs or actions, does it mean that we are at the same time rejecting them as a person?

To Take Away

Suggestions For Your Quiet Times This Week:

Ask the Holy Spirit to guide you into all truth and to reveal to your mind the lies you have believed as a result of having been brought up with a non-biblical worldview.

Big Question (to consider before the next session):

If we share God's nature and we are saints, why do you think it is that we still feel such a pull to ways of thinking and behaving that go against God's best?

Session 5
Our Daily Choice

Focus Verse

Romans 8:9: You, however, are controlled not by the flesh but by the Spirit, if the Spirit of God lives in you.

Objective

To understand that, although we still have urges that tend to pull us away from relying completely on God and following the promptings of His Spirit, we no longer have to give in to them but are free to choose.

Focus Truth

Although you are a new person in Christ with a completely new nature, and are free to live according to what the Holy Spirit tells you, obeying Him is not automatic.

Welcome

What would you most like to do if you knew you could not fail?

Worship

Read together the My Father God statements from Session 2, then spend time worshipping God for who He is.

Word

What Did Happen When We Became Christians

- We have a new heart and a new Spirit within us
- We have new life "in Christ"
- We have a new master

What Did Not Happen

- Our body did not change

- Our "flesh" was not taken away

- Sin did not die

The law of sin is still effective. How can you overcome a law that is still effective? By a greater law: "Through Christ Jesus the law of the Spirit of life set me free from the law of sin and death" (Romans 8:2).

Our Choices

- even though we no longer have to think and react according to our flesh, we can choose to do so
- even though sin has no power over us, we can choose to give in to it

Nothing can change the fact of who we now are, and God's love for us, but the outcome of that in our day-to-day lives is down to our individual choice — are we going to choose to believe what God says is true and act on it, or not?

Three Different Types Of Person (1 Corinthians 2:14-3:3)

The Natural Person
("the man without the Spirit") - 1 Corinthians 2:14 & Ephesians 2:1-3

This describes someone who is not yet a Christian:
• physically alive but spiritually dead
• separated from God
• living independently from God
• lives in the flesh; actions and choices dictated by the flesh
  (see Galatians 5:19-21)
• has no spiritual basis for coping with life's stresses

The Spiritual Person - 1 Corinthians 2:15

The normal state for a Christian:
• has been transformed through faith in Christ
• spirit is now united with God's Spirit
• has received:
        - forgiveness
        - acceptance in God's family
        - realisation of worth in Christ
• receives impetus from God's Spirit instead of the flesh
• is renewing the mind (ie getting rid of the old patterns
of thinking and replacing them with truth)
• emotions marked by joy and peace instead of turmoil
• chooses to walk in the Spirit and therefore
demonstrates the fruit of the Spirit. (Galatians 5:22,23)
• still has the flesh but crucifies it daily as he recognises the truth that he
is now dead to sin (Romans 6:11-14)

"His divine power has given us everything we need for life and godliness
through our knowledge of him who called us by his own glory and
goodness" (2 Peter 1:3).

The Fleshly Person - 1 Corinthians 3:3

A Christian who has been made spiritually alive but, instead of choosing to follow the impulses of the Spirit, follows the impulses of the flesh.

His daily life tends to mimic that of the natural (non-Christian) person rather than the spiritual person:
• mind occupied by wrong thoughts
• emotions plagued by negative feelings
• body showing signs of stress
• feelings of inferiority, insecurity, inadequacy, guilt, worry and doubt

Pause For Thought 1
Does it surprise you that a Christian can live very much like a non-Christian?
Why do you think many Christians are plagued by insecurity, inferiority, inadequacy, guilt, worry and doubt?
Is it really possible for every Christian to rise above the law of sin and overcome the flesh?

Barriers To Growth

• Ignorance

• Deception

Colossians 2:6-8: "So then, just as you received Christ Jesus as Lord, continue to live in him, rooted and built up in him, strengthened in the faith as you were taught, and overflowing with thankfulness. See to it that no one takes you captive through hollow and deceptive philosophy, which depends on human tradition and the basic principles of this world rather than on Christ."

Common areas of deception:
      • "this might work for others, but my case is different and it won't work for me"

- "I could never have faith like so and so"
- "God could never use me"

• Unresolved personal and spiritual conflicts

Many have come to faith but have not repented.

The Steps to Freedom In Christ are a tool you can use to examine your life and ask the Holy Spirit to show you areas where you have not repented and closed the door to the enemy's influence.

Pause For Thought 2
Do you sense that you are growing as a Christian as quickly as you could be?
What barriers do you suspect there might be in your own life? (You might like to spend some time asking the Holy Spirit to show you.)

Choosing To Walk By The Spirit Every Day

Once we have committed ourselves to believe truth no matter what we feel, and we have dealt with our unresolved spiritual conflicts, we are genuinely free to make a choice every day. We can choose to obey either the promptings of the flesh or the promptings of the Holy Spirit. The two are in direct opposition to each other.

Walking By The Spirit Is *Not*:

• Just a good feeling

• A licence to do whatever we want

"The flesh desires what is contrary to the Spirit, and the Spirit what is contrary to the flesh. They are in conflict with each other." (Galatians 5:17)

• Legalism

"If you are led by the Spirit, you are not under law." (Galatians 5:18)

Walking By The Spirit *Is:*

• True freedom

"Where the Spirit of the Lord is, there is freedom." (2 Corinthians 3:17)

• Being led

"My sheep listen to my voice; I know them, and they follow me." (John 10:27)

• Walking at God's pace

"Come to me, all you who are weary and burdened, and I will give you rest. Take my yoke upon you and learn from me, for I am gentle and humble in heart, and you will find rest for your souls. For my yoke is easy and my burden is light." (Matthew 11:28-30)

How Can We Tell If We Are Walking By The Spirit?

Just as you can tell a tree by its fruit, you can tell whether you are walking by the Spirit by the fruit of your life (see Galatians 5:19-23).

Witness

How would you explain to a non-Christian the benefits of being filled with the Spirit in a way that would make sense to them?

Questions For Groups

1. Does it surprise you to see that a Christian can live very much like a non-Christian?

2. Why do you think many Christians are plagued by insecurity, inferiority, inadequacy, guilt, worry and doubt?

3. Why do you think so many Christians live so far below their potential in Christ?

4. Is it really possible for every Christian to rise above the law of sin and defeat the flesh?

5. Do you sense that you are growing as a Christian as quickly as you could be?

6. What barriers do you suspect there might be in your own life? You might like to spend some time asking the Holy Spirit to show you.

7. How can you tell if you are filled with the Spirit?

To Take Away

Suggestions For Your Quiet Times This Week:
Every day, specifically commit yourself to walk by the Spirit and ask the Holy Spirit to fill you.

Big Question (to consider before the next session):
Read Romans 6:1-7. This passage says that we have "died to sin" and should "no longer be slaves to sin". Have you ever experienced being caught in a pattern of behaviour that you knew was wrong but from which you seemed unable to escape? Or have you found yourself apparently unable to do something good that you knew was right?

Session 6
Demolishing Strongholds

Focus Verse

2 Corinthians 10:5: We demolish arguments and every pretension that sets itself up against the knowledge of God, and we take captive every thought to make it obedient to Christ.

Objective

To understand what "strongholds" are and where they come from so that we can dismantle them by renewing our minds.

Focus Truth

All of us have mental strongholds, ways of thinking that are not in line with God's truth.

Welcome

What is the nastiest thing anyone ever said to you or about you? Were you able to shrug it off or did it stick with you?

Worship

Suggested theme: God's grace. See Ephesians 1:7,8; 1 John 3: 1,2.

Word

Strongholds

"It is for freedom that Christ has set us free." (Galatians 5:1)

If you're not connecting with the truth, it's probably because of mental "strongholds" and a lack of repentance.

Ed Silvoso defines a stronghold as:
"A mind-set impregnated with hopelessness that causes us to accept as unchangeable situations that we know are contrary to the will of God." (*That None Should Perish*, Ed Silvoso, Regal Books, 1994, p.155)

Strongholds are mental habit patterns of thought that are not consistent with God's word. They usually show themselves in something less than Christ-like temperament or behaviour.

Pause For Thought 1
Does it ever feel as if you can't do what you know God wants you to do, or stop doing something you know God wants you to stop?
If something is against God's will, can it be changed? Or, to ask the question a different way, do you think God dangles impossible things before us like a cruel father who tells us to do something that he knows we just cannot do?

How Strongholds Are Established

Our Environment

The fallen world we live in is hostile to God
- we lived in it every day before we knew Christ
- we have been conditioned to conform to it

Traumatic Experiences

Eg a death in the home, a divorce or a rape. They set up strongholds because of their intensity.

Temptation

Strongholds are also formed or reinforced when we repeatedly give in to temptation. Every temptation is an attempt to get you to live your life independently of God. The basis for that temptation is often legitimate needs. The question is: are those needs going to be met by responding to the world, the flesh and the devil, or are they going to be met by Christ who promises to "meet all your needs according to his glorious riches in Christ Jesus" (Philippians 4:19)?

"Threshold Thinking"

"No temptation has seized you except what is common to man. And God is faithful; he will not let you be tempted beyond what you can bear. But when you are tempted, he will also provide a way out so that you can stand up under it." (1 Corinthians 10:13)

God has provided a way of escape from all temptation — it's right at the beginning when the tempting thought first comes into your mind. That's your opportunity to "take captive every thought to make it obedient to Christ" (2 Corinthians 10:5).

Pause For Thought 2
Has it ever felt as if there is no way out of temptation? How can you prepare yourself for future temptation?

Effects Of Strongholds

Faulty View Of Reality

"As the heavens are higher than the earth, so are my ways higher than your ways and my thoughts than your thoughts." (Isaiah 55:9)

"Trust in the Lord with all your heart and lean not on your own understanding. In all your ways acknowledge him, and he will make your paths straight." (Proverbs 3:5-6)

Strongholds tend to prevent us seeing what is really true because of how they make us feel.

Bad Choices

How easy do you find it to choose to believe what God says is true even when it doesn't feel true? Can you think of an example of when you have done this and say what the outcome was?

Demolishing Strongholds

Do we have to put up with strongholds? No!

"For though we live in the world we do not wage war as the world does. The weapons we fight with are not the weapons of the world. On the contrary, they have divine power to demolish strongholds. We demolish arguments and every pretension that sets itself up against the knowledge of God, and we take every thought captive to make it obedient to Christ." (2 Corinthians 10:3-5)

A Whole Answer

If we want a whole answer, we need to understand that we are up against not only the world and the flesh but also the devil. In the next session we will look at the role of the devil, which is, in fact, the easiest of the three to resolve.

Witness

How easy do you find it to talk about Jesus to those who don't yet know Him? Do you think that any difficulty might be something to do with strongholds in your mind? Try to work out what lies might be in operation and find some truth in the Bible to commit yourself to.

Questions For Groups

1. Do you feel that you are "connecting" with truth as much as you would like to?

2. Do you ever think that you have settled for a "second-best" Christian life?

3. One definition of a stronghold is "anything you know is right that you can't do, or anything that you know is wrong that you can't stop doing". If you find yourself doing something that is not in line with God's will, can you stop? Or, to ask the question a different way, do you think God dangles impossible things before us like a cruel father who tells us to do something that he knows we just cannot do?

4. Has it ever felt as if there is no way out of temptation?

5. How can you prepare yourself for future temptation?

6. How easy do you find it to choose to believe what God says is true even when it doesn't feel true? Can you give an example of when you have done this and say what the outcome was?

To Take Away

Suggestions For Your Quiet Times This Week:

Meditate on these passages: 2 Corinthians 10:3-5; Romans 8:35-39; Philippians 4:12-13.

Big Question (to consider before the next session):

How has Satan deceived you in the past? How is he deceiving you right now?

Session 7
The Battle For Our Minds

Focus Verse

Ephesians 6:11: Put on the full armour of God so that you can take your stand against the devil's schemes.

Objective

To understand that, although the devil is constantly attempting to get us to believe lies, we don't have to believe every thought that comes into our head but can hold each one up against the truth and choose to accept or reject it.

Focus Truth

The battle takes place in our minds. If we are aware of how Satan works, we will not fall for his schemes.

Welcome

Has anyone ever played a really good trick on you, or have you played one on someone else?

Worship

Suggested theme: God's authority. See 1 John 3:8; Colossians 2:15; Matthew 28:18,19.

Word

The Battle Is Real

Jesus came to destroy the devil's work (1 John 3:8).

The tendency of those of us brought up with the Western worldview is to dismiss the reality of the spiritual world or act as if it does not exist. Paul tells us explicitly that we are not fighting flesh and blood but the spiritual forces of wickedness in the heavenly realms (Ephesians 6:10ff).

Who Is Satan?

Adam and Eve effectively handed over their right to rule the world to Satan, whom Jesus called "the prince (ruler) of this world" (John 12:31).

Satan Is Not Like God

We tend to divide the world into "natural" and "supernatural", but the Bible makes the distinction between "Creator" and "created" (see John 1:3). Like us, Satan is a created being, whereas God is the Creator. There is no comparison between them.

Satan Can Be In Only One Place At One Time

Because Satan is a created being we can infer that he can be only in one place at one time. Only God is everywhere at once.

Satan's Power And Authority Do Not Even Begin To Compare To God's

At the cross Jesus completely disarmed Satan (Colossians 2:15). Jesus is now "far above" all powers and authorities (Ephesians 1:21).

Satan Does Not Know Everything

Satan cannot perfectly read your mind. We can infer this from the Bible (eg Daniel 2, where sorcerers using demonic powers could not read Nebuchadnezzar's mind) and from the fact that Satan is a created being and does not possess the attributes of God.

How Satan Works

Through An Organised Network Of Fallen Angels

Satan works through "rulers, authorities, powers and spiritual forces of evil in the heavenly realms" (Ephesians 6:12).

By Putting Thoughts Into Our Minds

"The Spirit clearly says that in later times some will abandon the faith and follow deceiving spirits and things taught by demons." (1 Timothy 4:1)

"Satan rose up against Israel and incited David to take a census of Israel." (1 Chronicles 21:1)

"The evening meal was being served, and the devil had already prompted Judas Iscariot, son of Simon, to betray Jesus." (John 13:2)

"Then Peter said, 'Ananias, how is it that Satan has so filled your heart that you have lied to the Holy Spirit and have kept for yourself some of the money you received for the land?'" (Acts 5:3)

If Satan can put thoughts into our minds, he can make them sound like our own: "*I'm* useless; *I'm* ugly."

Pause For Thought 1

Have any of the things you have learned so far about Satan surprised you? Does he now seem more or less powerful than you had imagined?

Is it a surprise to you that some of the thoughts in your mind may have been put there by a deceiving spirit even though they seem like your own thoughts? Can you identify some of them? Are they completely false or is there some truth in them?

Through Temptation, Accusation And Deception

If I tempt you, you know it. If I accuse you, you know it. But if I deceive you, by definition you don't know it. Deception is Satan's primary strategy.

By Getting Footholds In Our Lives Through Sin

Ephesians 4:26-27 says that if you do not deal with your anger in short order, you give the devil a foothold in your life.

"If you forgive anyone, I also forgive him. And what I have forgiven — if there was anything to forgive — I have forgiven in the sight of Christ for your sake, in order that Satan might not outwit us. For we are not unaware of his schemes." (2 Corinthians 2:10-11)

Satan's greatest access to Christians is often through the sin of unforgiveness.

The Relationship Between Demons And Christians

We are not talking about Christians being "possessed", ie completely taken over or taken back by demons. At the centre of your being, your spirit is connected to God's Spirit and Satan can't have you back. We're talking about Satan gaining an amount of influence in your mind so that he can neutralise you or even use you to further his agenda.

Temptation, Accusation, Deception
⇩
INFLUENCED (probable)
(1 Peter 5:8)
USED TO FURTHER SATAN'S AGENDA (possible)
(Acts 5:3)
OWNED (never)
(1 Peter 2:18-18)

Our Defence

Understand Our Position In Christ

Ephesians 1:19-22 tells us that Jesus is seated at God's right hand, the ultimate seat of power and authority, "far above all rule and authority, power and dominion".

"And God raised us up with Christ and seated us *with Him* in the heavenly realms in Christ Jesus." (Ephesians 2:6)

Because of the finished work of Christ, the Church is given both the power and the authority to continue His work. Our authority is to do God's will, nothing more and nothing less. We also have God's mighty power as long as we are filled (controlled) by the Holy Spirit.

Even though he is defeated, Satan still "prowls around like a roaring lion looking for someone to devour" (1 Peter 5:8). Paul tells us to put on the armour of God and stand firm (Ephesians 6:11-20).

"Submit to God. Resist the devil, and he will flee from you." (James 4:7) This is the key for sin-confess cycles. Don't just confess but also resist the devil.

Do Not Be Frightened

Demons are petrified of Christians who know the extent of the power and authority they have in Christ.

"The one who was born of God keeps him safe, and the evil one cannot harm him." (1 John 5:18)

Guard Our Minds

"Prepare your minds for action." (1 Peter 1:13)

We are never told to direct our thoughts inwardly or passively but always outwardly and actively. God never bypasses our minds — He works through them.

Turn On The Light

Satan has no power over us at all unless he can deceive us into believing that he does — and we give him that power only when we fail to believe the truth.

Expose Satan's lie to God's truth, and his power is broken.

"My prayer is not that you take them out of the world but that you protect them from the evil one. Sanctify them by the truth; your word is truth." (John 17:16-17)

Trying not to think negative thoughts doesn't work. As Christians we are not called to dispel the darkness. We are instructed to turn on the light. Rather than concentrating on getting rid of the darkness, fill your mind with light.

"Do not be anxious about anything, but in everything, by prayer and petition, with thanksgiving, present your requests to God. And the peace of God, which transcends all understanding, will guard your hearts and your minds in Christ Jesus. Finally, brothers, whatever is true, whatever is noble, whatever is right, whatever is pure, whatever is lovely, whatever is admirable — if anything is excellent or praiseworthy — think about such things." (Philippians 4:6-8)

Pause For Thought 2
Read Ephesians 6:10-20. What do you think it means in
practice to put on the armour of God? Is it just saying the
words or is there more to it than that?
If you woke up in the night with the feeling that there was a
scary demonic presence in your bedroom, based on James 4:7
and what you have learned, what do you think would be a
good course of action?

Witness

How do you think Satan works in the lives of your non-Christian friends? What might you be able to do about this?

Questions For Groups

1. Have any of the things you have learned so far about Satan surprised you?

2. Does he now seem more or less powerful than you had imagined?

3. Is it a surprise to you that some of the thoughts in your mind might have been put there by a deceiving spirit even though they seem like your own?

4. Can you identify some thoughts that you have had that you now think might be from the enemy? Are they completely false or is there some truth in them?

5. Read Ephesians 6:10-20. What do you think it means in practice to "put on the armour of God"? Is it just saying the words or is there more to it than that?

6. If you woke up in the night with the feeling that there was a scary demonic presence in your bedroom, based on James 4:7 and what you have learned in this session, what do you think would be a good course of action?

To Take Away

Suggestions For Your Quiet Times This Week:

Meditate on the following verses: Matthew 28:18; Ephesians 1:3-14; Ephesians 2:6-10; Colossians 2:13-15.

Big Question (to consider before the next session):

If we can't always trust what we feel, why has God given us feelings and how should we respond to them?

Session 8
Handling Emotions Well

Focus Verse

1 Peter 5:7,8: Cast all your anxiety on him because he cares for you. Be self-controlled and alert. Your enemy the devil prowls around like a roaring lion looking for someone to devour.

Objective

To understand our emotional nature and how it is related to what we believe.

Focus Truth

Our emotions are essentially a product of our thoughts and a barometer of our spiritual health.

Welcome

Would you describe yourself as an emotional person?
Tell the group about an event in the past that resulted in emotional pain or joy.

Worship

Suggested theme: God's heart for His people. Isaiah 1:10-20; Isaiah 40:1-2; Philippians 2:5-8.

Word

We Can't Directly Control How We Feel

Link Between The Inner And Outer Person

Our soul/spirit was designed to function in union with our body. The obvious correlation is between the brain and the mind.

The brain functions like computer hardware. The mind is like the software. In the Bible the overwhelming emphasis is on the mind: choosing truth, believing the truth, taking every thought captive, and so on.

What We Can And Cannot Control

We cannot directly control our feelings but we can in fact change our emotions over time by choosing to change what we can control: what we believe and how we behave.

Our Feelings Reveal What We Really Believe

Our emotions are to our soul what our ability to feel pain is to our body.

If what you believe does not reflect truth, then what you feel will not reflect reality. Life's events don't determine who you are or what you feel — it's your perception of those events.

The more we commit ourselves to the truth and choose to believe what God says is true, the more we will see our circumstances from God's perspective and the less our feelings will run away with us.

Changing How We Feel

The main cause of stress is that we have come to believe through past experiences or failures that we are helpless or hopeless.
But no Christian is helpless or hopeless.

Pause For Thought 1
Do you agree that it's not your circumstances that determine how you feel but how you see those circumstances?
If you tend to feel overwhelmed by negative emotions, how might you start to make sure that you are looking at your circumstances in a healthy way that reflects what is actually true?

Following Feelings Makes Us Vulnerable To Attack

You don't feel your way into good behaviour. You behave your way into good feelings. We start by choosing to believe the truth which works itself out in our behaviour. This then over time leads to a change in our feelings.

A failure to handle emotions such as anger (see Ephesians 4:26-27) and anxiety (see 1 Peter 5:7-9) in the right way sets us up for problems.

Three Ways To Handle Emotions

Cover It Up (Suppression)

Suppression is when we consciously ignore our feelings or choose not to deal with them. There are two problems with that — it's unhealthy and it's dishonest.

Explode (Indiscriminate Expression)

Indiscriminate expression is unhealthy for those around us.

"Everyone should be quick to listen, slow to speak and slow to become angry, for man's anger does not bring about the righteous life that God desires." (James 1:19,20)

Be Honest (Acknowledgment)

The healthy response is to be honest and acknowledge how we feel, first to God but also to others.

Pause For Thought 2
Look at Psalm 109:6-15. Have you ever felt like David? Have you ever prayed like that? Would it be right to pray like that? Is there anything that you feel you could not say to God that He does not already know?

Handling Past Traumas

God doesn't want emotional pain from our past to influence us negatively today.

Children of God are not primarily products of their past. They are primarily products of Christ's work on the cross and His resurrection. Nobody can fix our past, but we can be free from it. We can re-evaluate our past from the perspective of who we are now in Christ. God sets us free as we forgive from our hearts those people who have offended us.

Witness

If you are feeling angry, anxious or depressed, do you think it would be better not to let that show to non-Christians around you in case you are a bad advertisement for Jesus Christ? Or do you think it might be better for them to see you as you really are?

Questions For Groups

1. Suppose someone had the power to take away the sensation of pain and offered it to you as a gift. Would you receive it?

2. Do you agree that it's not your circumstances that determine how you feel but how you look at those circumstances?

3. If you tend to feel overwhelmed by negative emotions, how might you start to make sure you are looking at your circumstance in a healthy way that reflects what is actually true?

4. When something triggers a strong emotion in you do you tend to cover it up, explode or acknowledge it?

5. Read Psalm 109:6-15. Does it surprise you that something like that is in the Bible? Remember, this is the holy, inspired, perfect word of God! Have you ever felt like David? Have you ever prayed like that? Would it be right to pray like that?

6. Is there anything that you feel you could not say to God that He does not already know?

To Take Away

Suggestions For Your Quiet Times This Week:

Consider the emotional nature of the Apostle Peter. First, have a look at some occasions where he let his emotions run away with him and acted or spoke too hastily: Matthew 16:21-23; Matthew 17:1-5; John 18:1-11. Second, look at how Jesus was able to look beyond these emotional outbursts and see his potential: Matthew 16:17-19. Finally, see how that came true when Peter, under the power of the Holy Spirit, became the spokesperson of the early church: Acts 2:14-41. Nothing in your character is so big that God cannot make something good out of it!

Big Question (to consider before the next session):

Think of the worst thing anyone ever did to you (you will not be asked to share it). Why should you forgive that person? Can you think of any good reasons why you shouldn't forgive someone?

Session 9
Forgiving From The Heart

Focus Verse

Matthew 18:34-35: In anger his master turned him over to the jailers to be tortured, until he should pay back all he owed. This is how my heavenly Father will treat each of you unless you forgive your brother from your heart.

Objective

To recognise what forgiveness is and what it is not, and to learn how to forgive from the heart.

Focus Truth

In order to experience our freedom in Christ, we need to relate to other people in the same way that God relates to us — on the basis of complete forgiveness and acceptance.

Welcome

Read Matthew 18:21-25 or act it out using the script on page 72. Then try to put yourself in the place of one of the characters and say what strikes you most about the story.

Worship

Suggested theme: God's forgiveness of us (Psalm 103:1-12; Hebrews 10:19-22).

Word

The Need To Forgive

"If you forgive anyone, I also forgive him. And what I have forgiven — if there was anything to forgive — I have forgiven in the sight of Christ for your sake, in order that Satan might not outwit us. For we are not unaware of his schemes." (2 Corinthians 2:10-11)

Nothing keeps you in bondage to the past more than an unwillingness to forgive. Nothing gives Satan greater opportunity to stop a church growing than roots of bitterness, the evidence of personal unforgiveness, and pride.

It Is Required By God (Matthew 6:9-15)

We must learn to relate to others on the same basis that God relates to us.

It Is Essential For Our Freedom (Matthew 18:21-35)

We need to understand the extent of our own debt. Those who have been forgiven much love much. Those who have been forgiven little love little.

Pause For Thought 1
Do you sometimes feel that your sins weren't "that bad" compared to others'?
How much have you been forgiven? Little or much?

• Repayment is impossible

• Mercy is required

• So that no advantage can be taken of you (2 Corinthians 2:10-11)

What Does It Mean To Forgive From The Heart?

Jesus warns that, if you do not forgive from your heart, you will suffer some kind of spiritual torment.

We recommend a formula: "Lord, I choose to forgive (name)_____for (specifically identify every remembered pain and hurt inflicted on you)_____, which made me feel_____".

Forgiveness must be extended to others (Ephesians 4:31-32). However, the crisis is only between God and us.

We Forgive To Stop The Pain

It is for our sake that we forgive. "But you don't know how much that hurt me." Don't you see that they are still hurting you? How do you stop the pain? By forgiving.

We think that by forgiving someone we let them off the hook — but by not forgiving them we stay hooked to the pain and the past.

Pause For Thought 2
Naturally speaking, none of us would want to remember past hurts. Is it necessary to do so in order genuinely to forgive? Do you agree that the crisis of forgiveness is between you and God rather than between you and the other person? Does it feel like that?
Who continues to feel pain when there is no forgiveness: the offender or the offended?

What is Forgiveness?

Not Forgetting
You can't get rid of a hurt simply by trying to forget it.

Not Tolerating Sin

Not Seeking Revenge
"Do not take revenge, my friends, but leave room for God's wrath, for it is written: 'It is mine to avenge; I will repay,' says the Lord." (Romans 12:19)

The justice is in the cross.

Resolving To Live With The Consequences Of Sin

Everybody is living with the consequences of somebody else's sin. The only real choice we have is to do that in the bondage of bitterness or the freedom of forgiveness.

Forgiveness is to set a captive free and then realise that *you* were the captive.

Pause For Thought 3
How has this session changed your view of what forgiveness is or is not?
Next time someone offends you, will you be quicker to forgive? Why/why not?

Witness

How might this question of forgiveness challenge someone who is not yet a Christian? Are there any ways you can demonstrate forgiveness to someone who does not yet know the Lord?

Questions For Groups

1. How much have you been forgiven? Little or much?

2. Do you sometimes feel that your sins weren't "that bad" compared to others'?

3. Naturally speaking, none of us would want to remember past hurts. Is it necessary to do so in order to truly forgive?

4. Do you agree that the crisis of forgiveness is between you and God rather than between you and the other person? Does it feel like that?

5. Who continues to feel pain when there is no forgiveness: the offender or the offended?

6. How has this session changed your view of what forgiveness is or is not?

7. Next time someone offends you, will you be quicker to forgive? Why/why not?

To Take Away

Suggestions For Your Quiet Times This Week:

Ask the Holy Spirit to prepare your heart by leading you into all truth and starting to reveal to you the areas you will need to bring into the light when you go through The Steps To Freedom In Christ.

Big Question (to consider before the next session):

Have you grown as a Christian as quickly as you would have liked? If not, what do you think has got in the way?

Dramatisation Of Matthew 18:21-25

Characters:	Peter, Jesus, Servant 1, Servant 2, Master

Peter
: Lord, how many times shall I forgive my brother when he sins against me? Up to seven times?

Jesus
: I tell you, not seven times, but seventy-seven times.

Therefore, the kingdom of heaven is like a king who wanted to settle accounts with his servants. As he began the settlement, a man who owed him ten thousand talents was brought to him. Since he was not able to pay, the master ordered that he and his wife and his children and all that he had be sold to repay the debt.

The servant fell on his knees before him.

Servant 1
: Be patient with me, and I will pay back everything.

Jesus
: The servant's master took pity on him, cancelled the debt and let him go. But when that servant went out, he found one of his fellow servants who owed him a hundred denarii. He grabbed him and began to choke him.

Servant 1
: Pay back what you owe me!

Jesus
: His fellow servant fell to his knees and begged him:

Servant 2
: Be patient with me, and I will pay you back.

Jesus
: But he refused. Instead, he went off and had the man thrown into prison until he could pay the debt. When the other servants saw what had happened, they were greatly distressed and went and told their master everything that had happened.

Then the master called the servant in.

Master	You wicked servant, I cancelled all that debt of yours because you begged me to. Shouldn't you have had mercy on your fellow servant just as I had on you?
Jesus	In anger his master turned him over to the jailers to be tortured, until he should pay back all he owed.
	This is how my heavenly Father will treat each of you unless you forgive your brother from your heart.

Steps To Forgiveness

1. Ask the Lord to reveal to your mind the people you need to forgive

Make a list of everyone the Lord brings to your mind. Ask the Holy Spirit to guide you and write the names on a separate piece of paper. Even if you think there is no one, just ask God to bring up all the right names.

The two most overlooked are yourself and God.

Forgiving yourself

Only God can forgive your sins — but for many people, especially perfectionists, the hardest person for them to forgive is themselves, for letting themselves down. You are in effect accepting God's forgiveness and refusing to listen to the devil's accusations. Some people are really helped by being able to say, "I forgive myself for (list everything you hold against yourself), and I let myself off my own hook."

Forgiving God
Forgiving God is harder to understand because God has done nothing wrong. He has always acted in your best interests.

Because you have not understood God's larger plan, or because you have blamed God for something that other people or the devil have done, you may have felt that God has let you down.

Many people feel disappointed with God, even angry with Him, because He didn't answer their prayer; He didn't seem to be there for them. They cried out for help and nothing came. Usually they are embarrassed to admit it. But God knows anyway and He's big enough to handle it.

If you feel uncomfortable telling God you forgive Him, say something like, "I release the expectations, thoughts and feelings I have had against you."

2. Acknowledge the hurt and the hate

Jesus instructed us to forgive from the heart. That's much more than simply saying "I forgive" and pretending we've dealt with it. To forgive from the heart we need to face the hurt and the hate. People try to suppress their emotional pain, but it is trying to surface so that we can let it go.

3. Understand the significance of the cross
The cross is what makes forgiveness legally and morally right.

Jesus has already taken upon Himself your sins and the sins of the person who has hurt you. He died "once for all" (Hebrews 10:10). When your heart says, "It isn't fair", remember that the justice is in the cross.

4. Decide that you will bear the burden of each person's sin
You need to make a choice not to use the information you have against that person in the future.

"He who covers over an offence promotes love, but whoever repeats the matter separates close friends." (Proverbs 17:9)

That doesn't mean you never testify in a court of law — however, you do it not in the bitterness of unforgiveness but having first forgiven from your heart.

5. Decide to forgive
Forgiveness is a crisis of the will. If you wait until you feel like doing it, you probably never will.

You may feel you can't do it — but would God really tell you to do something you couldn't do? When he says that you can do all things in Christ, is that true or not? The reality is that you have a choice to make — are you going to remain in bitterness, hooked to the past, giving the enemy an entrance to your mind; or are you going to get rid of it once and for all?

You choose to forgive, and in making that choice you are agreeing to live with sin and its consequences. You are choosing to let God be the avenger, and trust Him to bring justice in the end. You choose to take it to the cross and leave it there.

The gates of hell can't prevail against the kingdom of God. There is nobody out there keeping you from being the person that God created you to be. The only one that can do that is you. You need to forgive, be merciful and love as Christ has loved you. Let that person go; get on with your life; walk away free in Christ.

6. Take your list to God

To forgive from your heart, say: "Lord, I choose to forgive my father" and then specify what you are forgiving him for. Stay with the same person until you have told the Lord every pain and hurt that has surfaced and be as specific as you can. It's then helpful to take it a step further and say how it made you feel: "I choose to forgive my father for leaving us, which made me feel abandoned."

Tears will often come at this point, but this is not about trying to get somebody to cry. It's making sure that it's as thorough as possible. One lady said, "I can't forgive my mother. I hate her." Having recognised her real feelings of hatred, now for the first time she probably could forgive — if she didn't admit that she hated her, she couldn't forgive.

Pray as follows for each person you need to forgive: "Lord, I choose to forgive (name the person) for (what they did or failed to do), which made me feel (verbally tell the Lord every hurt and pain He brings to your mind)".

Take careful note of what is said after the statement "which made me feel". What often occurs is repeated patterns (eg "abandoned", "stupid", "dirty"). You can tear down those strongholds by saying, for example: "I renounce the lie that I am stupid. I announce the truth that I have the mind of Christ" (1 Corinthians 2:16); "I renounce the lie that I am abandoned. I announce the truth that God has promised never to leave me nor forsake me" (Hebrews 13:5). We will look at a specific strategy for doing this in Session 10. There is space on page 78 for you to write down what comes up.

7. Destroy the list

You are now free from those people and those events in the past.

8. Do not expect that your decision to forgive will result in major changes in others

Forgiving others is primarily about you and your relationship with God. Pray for those you have forgiven, that they may be blessed and that they too may find the freedom of forgiveness (see Matthew 5:44; 2 Corinthians 2:7).

9. Try to understand the people you have forgiven

You may find it helpful to understand some of what the other person was going through, but don't go so far as to rationalise away the sin — this is not about saying "It didn't matter", because it did.

10. Expect positive results of forgiveness in you

Forgiveness is not about feeling good; it's about being free. However, good feelings will follow eventually. You will need to concentrate on renewing your mind so that negative ways of thinking are replaced by the truth.

11. Thank God for the lessons you have learned and the maturity you have gained

You are now free to move on and grow as a Christian.

12. Accept your part of the blame for the offences you suffered

Confess your part in any sin and know that you are forgiven. If you realise that someone has something against you, go to them and be reconciled. Confess your own wrongdoing rather than bringing up anything they did.

(Based on *Victory Over The Darkness*, Neil Anderson, Monarch, 2004)

Uncovering Strongholds

As you go through Step 3 (Forgiveness) of The Steps To Freedom In Christ, you are encouraged to pray as follows for each person you need to forgive: "Lord, I choose to forgive (name the person) for (what they did or failed to do), which made me feel (verbally tell the Lord every hurt and pain He brings to your mind)".

Use this page to record the things you say after "which made me feel". Some of them will reveal mental strongholds that you can work on. Session 10 will equip you with a strategy for this.

Session 10
Walking In Freedom Every Day

Focus Verse
Hebrews 5:14: But solid food is for the mature, who by constant use have trained themselves to distinguish good from evil.

Objective
To help people understand that taking hold of their freedom in Christ is not a one-off experience — it needs to become a way of life — and to provide them with tools to help.

Focus Truth
Our success in continuing to walk in freedom and grow in maturity depends on the extent to which we continue to renew our minds and train ourselves to distinguish good from evil.

Welcome
How did you find The Steps To Freedom In Christ process?
Or
How long have you been a Christian?

Worship
Take the theme of "freedom". See Galatians 5:1-12; Romans 8:1,2.

Word

Barriers To Maturity

"Brothers, I could not address you as spiritual but as worldly — mere infants in Christ. I gave you milk, not solid food, for you were not yet ready for it. Indeed, you are still not ready. You are still worldly. For since there is jealousy and quarrelling among you, are you not worldly?" (1 Corinthians 3:1-3)

Not Taking Hold Of Our Spiritual Freedom

"His divine power has given us everything we need for life and godliness through our knowledge of him who called us by his own glory and goodness." (2 Peter 1:3)

There is a great difference between freedom — which can be obtained in a relatively short time — and maturity, which is the work of a lifetime.

Freedom is a position we take in response to Christ's victory over sin and Satan. We are either free or bound in various areas of our lives. We don't grow into freedom in these areas: we take possession of freedom by the authority we have in Christ wherever we realise that we have been deceived and bound.

Not Taking Personal Responsibility

"It is for freedom that Christ has set us free. Stand firm, then, and do not let yourselves be burdened again by a yoke of slavery." (Galatians 5:1)

*Have you matured as a Christian as quickly as you would
like? What are some of the things that have hindered you?
Does it feel as if you already have everything you need? Have
you ever hoped that renewing your mind might be as simple
as asking God to "zap" you? Why does He tend not to do
this?*

Nothing and no one can prevent you from becoming the person God
wants you to be — except you!

Not Knowing The Basic Truths

"Though by this time you ought to be teachers, you need someone to
teach you the elementary truths of God's word all over again. You need
milk, not solid food! Anyone who lives on milk, being still an infant, is
not acquainted with the teaching about righteousness. But solid food is for
the mature, who by constant use have trained themselves to distinguish
good from evil." (Hebrews 5:12-14)

Faulty Thinking

Psychologists tell us that it takes around six weeks to form or break a
habit. Once you have dealt with any footholds of the enemy, a mental
stronghold is simply a habitual way of thinking. Can you break a habit?
Of course — but it takes some effort over a period of time.

Not Training Ourselves To Distinguish Good From Evil

Let's look again at something the writer to the Hebrews said:
"But solid food is for the mature, who by constant use have trained
themselves to distinguish good from evil." (Hebrews 5:14)

Strategies For Growth
Uncovering Lies

1. During The Steps To Freedom In Christ

2. Fear Appendix

Stronghold-Busting

1. Determine the lie you have been believing (any way you are thinking that is not in line with what God says about you in the Bible). In doing this, ignore what you feel but commit yourself wholeheartedly to God's truth.

2. Find as many Bible verses as you can that state the truth and write them down.

3. Write a prayer or declaration based on the formula:
>   I renounce the lie that...
>   I announce the truth that...

4. Finally, read the Bible verses and say the prayer/declaration every day for 40 days.

Pause For Thought 2
Take a lie and work out a "stronghold-buster". It might be really helpful to take a real lie that someone in the group has uncovered. Otherwise choose from this list: "I feel inferior"; "I feel that what I've done makes me unacceptable to God"; "I can't stop doing something that I know is wrong (choose something specific)"; "I am a failure"; "I know this works for others but it won't work for me".

Taking A Long-Term View

"Forgetting what is behind and straining towards what is ahead, I press on towards the goal to win the prize for which God has called me heavenwards in Christ Jesus. All of us who are mature should take such a view of things." (Philippians 3:13b-15a)

Other Practical Steps

Read *Walking In Freedom* by Neil Anderson

Accountability relationship

Do the teaching again!

Pause For Thought 3
What practical steps are you going to take to maintain your freedom and continually renew your mind?

Example Of A "Stronghold-Buster"

Taking Comfort In Food Rather Than God

The lie: that overeating brings lasting comfort.

Proverbs 25:28
Like a city whose walls are broken down is a man who lacks self-control.

Galatians 5:16
So I say, live by the Spirit, and you will not gratify the desires of the sinful nature.

Galatians 5:22
But the fruit of the Spirit is love, joy, peace, patience, kindness, goodness, faithfulness, gentleness and self-control. Against such things there is no law. Those who belong to Christ Jesus have crucified the sinful nature with its passions and desires.

2 Corinthians 1:3-4
Praise be to the God and Father of our Lord Jesus Christ, the Father of compassion and the God of all comfort, who comforts us in all our troubles, so that we can comfort those in any trouble with the comfort we ourselves have received from God.

Psalm 63:4-5
I will praise you as long as I live, and in your name I will lift up my hands. My soul will be satisfied as with the richest of foods; with singing lips my mouth will praise you.

Psalm 119:76
May your unfailing love be my comfort.

Lord, I renounce the lie that overeating brings lasting comfort. I announce the truth that you are the God of all comfort and that your unfailing love is my only legitimate and real comfort. I affirm that I now live by the Spirit and do not have to gratify the desires of the flesh. Whenever I feel in need of comfort, instead of turning to foods I choose to praise you and be satisfied as with the richest of foods. Fill me afresh with your Holy Spirit and live through me as I grow in self-control. Amen.

Tick off the days

1	2	3	4	5	6	7	8	9
10	11	12	13	14	15	16	17	18
19	20	21	22	23	24	25	26	27
28	29	30	31	32	33	34	35	36
37	38	39	40					

Witness

How would you explain to a not-yet Christian some of the things you have learned on this course?

Questions For Groups

1. Have you matured as a Christian as quickly as you would like? What are some of the things that have hindered you?

2. Read 2 Peter 1:3. Does it feel as if you already have everything you need to live the Christian life? Have you ever hoped that renewing your mind might be as simple as asking God to "zap" you? Why does He not tend to do this?

3. Take a lie and work out a "stronghold-buster". It might be really helpful to take a real lie that someone in the group has uncovered. Otherwise choose from this list:

   "I feel inferior"

   "I feel that what I've done makes me unacceptable to God"

   "I can't stop doing something that I know is wrong (choose something specific)"

   "I am a failure"

   "I know this stuff works for others but it won't work for me".

4. What practical steps are you going to take to maintain your freedom and continually renew your mind?

To Take Away

Suggestions For Your Quiet Times this week:

Work out a stronghold-buster for the most significant lie you have uncovered and start work on it.

Big Question (to consider before the next session):

When another Christian does something wrong, what would be a good way for you to respond? The Bible tells us not to judge others but it also makes clear that Christians sometimes need to be disciplined. What is the difference?

Session 11
Relating To Others

Focus Verse
Matthew 22:37-40: Jesus replied: "'Love the Lord your God with all your heart and with all your soul and with all your mind.' This is the first and greatest commandment. And the second is like it: 'Love your neighbour as yourself.' All the Law and the Prophets hang on these two commandments."

Objective
To understand our roles and responsibilities in relationships so that we can grow together in Christ.

Focus Truth
As a disciple of Christ we must assume responsibility for our own character and seek to meet the needs of others rather than the other way round.

Welcome
What is the thing that has struck you the most on this course so far?

Worship
Thank God for other people He has brought into your life.

Word

Understanding Grace

"'Love the Lord your God with all your heart and with all your soul and with all your mind.' This is the first and greatest commandment. And the second is like it: 'Love your neighbour as yourself.' All the Law and the Prophets hang on these two commandments." (Matthew 22:37-40)

We love because He first loved us (1 John 4:19).
We give freely because we have received freely (Matthew 10:8).
We are merciful because He has been merciful to us (Luke 6:36).
We forgive in the same way that Jesus has forgiven us (Ephesians 4:32).

We Are Responsible For Our Own Character And Others' Needs

"Who are you to judge someone else's servant? To his own master he stands or falls. And he will stand, for the Lord is able to make him stand." (Romans 14:4)

Each person is responsible before God for their own character.

"Do nothing out of selfish ambition or vain conceit, but in humility consider others better than yourselves. Each of you should look not only to your own interests, but also to the interests of others. Your attitude should be the same as that of Christ Jesus." (Philippians 2:3-5)

Where we do have a responsibility towards others before God, it is to meet the needs of others.

Being Aware Of Our Own Sins

When we see God for who He is, we don't become aware of the sin of others, but of our own sin. However, when we are lukewarm in our relationship with God, we tend to overlook our own sin and see the sin of others.

Focus On Responsibilities Rather Than Rights

In every relationship we have both rights and responsibilities — but where should we put the emphasis?

Do husbands have a right to expect their wives to be submissive to them? Or do they have a responsibility to love their wives as Christ loved the Church?

Do wives have a right to expect their husbands to love them? Or do they have a responsibility to love and respect their husbands who in turn have the responsibility of being the head of the home?

Do parents have a right to expect their children to be obedient? Or do they have a responsibility to bring them up in the training and instruction of the Lord, and to discipline them when they are disobedient?

Does being a member of a local church give you the right to criticise others? Or does it give you a responsibility to submit to those in authority over you and relate to one another with the same love and acceptance we have received from Christ?

When we emphasise our rights above our responsibilities in any relationship we sow the seeds of destruction.

Pause For Thought 1

What is our responsibility towards other people?
Why do we have a tendency to judge others and look out for our own needs?
If you find that you are becoming critical of others and unaware of your own sins, what is the problem and what can you do to put it right?

What About When Others Do Wrong?

Playing the role of the Holy Spirit in another person's life won't work.

Discipline Yes, Judgment No

Do not judge, or you too will be judged. For in the same way as you judge others, you will be judged, and with the measure you use, it will be measured to you. (Matthew 7:1)

Brothers, if someone is caught in a sin, you who are spiritual should restore him gently. (Galatians 6:1)

We are told not to judge, but we are to carry out discipline.

Judgment is always related to *character* whereas discipline is always related to *behaviour*.

Calling somebody "stupid", "clumsy", "proud" or "evil" is an attack on their character and it leaves them with no way forward.

If you point out someone's sinful behaviour, you are giving them something that they can work with: "You are right; what I just said wasn't true, and I am sorry."

Discipline And Punishment Are Not The Same

Punishment looks backwards, whereas discipline looks forwards.

God's discipline is a proof of His love (Hebrews 12:5-11).

The point of discipline is not to punish someone but to help them become more like Jesus.

Pause For Thought 2
Why shouldn't we be another person's conscience? What will happen if we try?
What is the difference between judgment and discipline?
What is the difference between discipline and punishment?

When We Are Attacked

"When they hurled their insults at him, he did not retaliate. When he suffered, he made no threats. Instead, he entrusted himself to him who judges justly." (1 Peter 2:23)

If you are wrong, you don't have a defence. If you are right, you don't need one. Christ is our defence.

Authority And Accountability

From which end of this list (top or bottom) did the Lord first come to you?

Authority

Accountability

Affirmation

Acceptance

"While we were still sinners, Christ died for us" (Romans 5:8). Acceptance came first, and then the affirmation: "The Spirit himself testifies with our spirit that we are God's children" (Romans 8:16). If authority figures demand accountability without giving affirmation and acceptance, they will never get it.

Should We Express Our Needs?

If we have needs in a relationship that are not being met, it is important that we let people know what they are. However, a need must be stated as a need, and not a judgment.

Pause For Thought 3
Should we be defensive if someone attacks our character?
Why or why not?
Have you experienced a time when authority figures
demanded accountability without first affirming and accepting
you? How did you respond to them? How will knowing this
affect what you do as a parent or in your church?
What needs do we all have? How can we share a need
without it backfiring on us?

One Of Life's Little Secrets

Every one of us needs to be loved, accepted and affirmed.

Jesus said, "It is more blessed to give than to receive" (Acts 20:35). We cannot sincerely help somebody else without helping ourselves in the process.

"Give and it will be given to you. A good measure, pressed down, shaken together and running over, will be poured into your lap. For with the measure you use, it will be measured to you." (Luke 6:38)

People are unreasonable, illogical and self-centred.
Love them anyway.
If you do good, people will accuse you of selfish, ulterior motives.
Do good anyway.
If you are successful, you will win false friends and true enemies.
Succeed anyway.
The good you do today will be forgotten tomorrow.
Do good anyway.
Honesty and frankness make you vulnerable.
Be honest and frank anyway.
The biggest people with the biggest ideas can be shot down by the
smallest people with the smallest minds.
Think big anyway.
People favour underdogs but follow only top dogs.
Fight for the underdog anyway.
What you spend years building may be destroyed overnight.
Build anyway.
People really need help, but may attack you if you help them.
Help people anyway.
Give the world the best you've got and you'll get kicked in the teeth.
Give the world the best you've got anyway.

Witness:

Being a positive witness is directly related to our capacity to love others. How can you be a good neighbour to those who live on your street, ie how can you love your neighbour as yourself? What needs do they have that you could help meet? How could you get to know them better, so that you would have a better idea of what their needs are? What needs do we all have?

Questions For Groups:

1. What is our responsibility towards other people?

2. Why do we have a tendency to judge others and look out for our own needs?

3. If you find that you are becoming critical of others and unaware of your own sins, what is the problem and what can you do to put it right?

4. Why shouldn't we be another person's conscience? What will happen if we try?

5. What happens if we emphasise rights over responsibilities?

6. What is the difference between judgment and discipline? What is the difference between discipline and punishment?

7. Should we be defensive if someone attacks our character? Why or why not?

8. Have you experienced a time when authority figures demanded accountability without first affirming and accepting you? How did you respond to them? How will knowing this affect what you do as a parent or in your church?

9. What needs do we all have? How can we share a need without it backfiring on us?

To Take Away

Suggestions For Your Quiet Times This Week:

Read Luke 6:27-41. This session may have convicted you of the need to relate differently to your family, friends and neighbours. You might want to seek the forgiveness of others. If you sense the Lord's conviction, then go to that person or persons and ask their forgiveness, stating clearly that what you have done is wrong. (Don't do this by letter or e-mail — it might be misunderstood or used against you.)

Big Question (to consider before the next session):

What are your goals for the rest of your life? How can you know if they are consistent with God's will?

Session 12
Where Are You Heading?

Focus Verse

1 Timothy 1:5: The goal of this command is love, which comes from a pure heart and a good conscience and a sincere faith.

Objective

To understand how faith relates to the goals and desires we have for our lives so that we can live a life of genuine freedom in Christ and become the person God created us to be.

Focus Truth

Nothing and no one can keep us from being the person God created us to be.

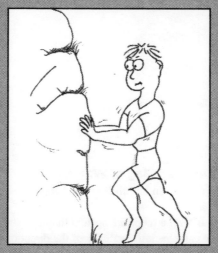

Welcome

What would you like to do before the end of your life?

Worship

Read John 10:28-29 and Jude 24-25. Praise God that He is able to complete the work that He started in you.

Word

Your Christian Walk Is The Result Of What You Believe

We have all come to believe that certain things will give us satisfaction, significance, fun, etc. But will they actually deliver the goods or are the goals we have developed faulty in some way?

Feelings Are God's Red Flag of Warning

Who knows best how we can be fulfilled and happy and peaceful? God!

God has equipped us with a feedback system that is designed to grab our attention so that we can check the validity of the direction we're heading in: our emotions.

When an experience or relationship leaves us feeling angry, anxious or depressed, those emotional signposts are there to alert us to the possibility that we may be working towards a faulty goal which is based on a wrong belief.

Anger Signals A Blocked Goal

Anxiety Signals An Uncertain Goal

Depression Signals An Impossible
Goal

Pause For Thought 1
Do you agree that your emotions can indicate whether your
goals are in line with God's will?
How do people typically respond to blocked goals? What has
been your tendency when you don't get your own way, or
someone or something is keeping you from doing what you
want to do?
Depression is often the result of negative perceptions of the
future, circumstances around us, and ourselves. How can
those perceptions (beliefs) be overcome by faith in God?

Wrong Responses When Our Goals Are Frustrated

If we believe that our sense of worth is dependent on other people and circumstances we will try to manipulate those people and circumstances.

Turning Bad Goals Into Good Goals

If God has a goal for your life, can it be blocked, or is its fulfilment uncertain or impossible? No!

No God-given goal can, therefore, be dependent on people or circumstances that we have no right or ability to control.

The Difference Between A "Goal" And A "Desire"

A godly goal is any specific orientation that reflects God's purpose for your life and does *not* depend on people or circumstances beyond your ability or right to control.

The only person who can block a godly goal or make it uncertain or impossible is you.

What do we do with a goal whose fulfilment is in itself a good thing but which depends on events or circumstances that we cannot control? We need to downgrade it in our thinking from a *goal,* upon which our whole sense of who we are depends, to what we might call "a godly desire".

A godly desire is any specific result that depends on the cooperation of other people, the success of events or favourable circumstances which you have no right or ability to control.

The Goal Is To Become the Person God Called You To Be

God Wants Us To Become Like Jesus
"It is God's will that you should be sanctified" (1 Thessalonians 4:3). Sanctification (becoming like Jesus) is God's will (goal) for our lives. Nobody and nothing on earth can keep you from being the person God called you to be.

The difficulties we face are actually a means of achieving our supreme goal of becoming more like Jesus:

"We rejoice in our sufferings, because we know that suffering produces perseverance; perseverance, character; and character, hope. And hope does not disappoint us, because God has poured out his love into our hearts by the Holy Spirit, whom he has given us." (Romans 5:3-5)

God's goal for our life is to do with our character — what we are *like* — rather than with what we *do*.

Pause For Thought 2
Can you see how differentiating between goals and desires can have a tremendous effect on you and your freedom? How?
What is God's primary goal for your life? Why can't it be blocked?
Is it liberating or convicting to know that nothing and no one can keep you from being the person God created you to be? Why?

When Our Goal Is Love

Paul says, "The goal of our instruction is love" (1 Timothy 1:5) (NASB). Love is the character of God, because God is love (1 John 4:7,8).

If you make godly character your primary goal then the fruit of the Spirit that will be produced in your life is love, joy (instead of depression), peace (instead of anxiety), and patience (instead of anger).

Witness:

Can distinguishing between goals and desires help you to be a more effective witness?

Questions For Groups:

1. Do you agree that your emotions can indicate whether your goals are in line with God's will?

2. How do people typically respond to blocked goals? What has been your tendency when you don't get your own way, or someone or something is keeping you from doing what you want to do?

3. Depression is often the result of negative perceptions of the future, circumstances around us, and ourselves. How can those perceptions (beliefs) be overcome by faith in God?

4. Can you see how differentiating between goals and desires can have a tremendous effect on you and your freedom? How?

5. What is God's primary goal for your life? Why can't it be blocked?

6. Is it liberating or convicting to know that nothing or anything can keep you from being the person God created you to be? Why?

To Take Away

Suggestions For Your Quiet Times This Week:

This coming week, take the time to evaluate your faith by completing the What Do I Believe? questions on page 104. You will not be asked to share how you are doing with the rest of the group. Give some serious thought as to how you would complete the sentences.

Big Question (to consider before the next session):

If you discover that your goals are not the same as God's goals for your life, would you be willing to change what you believe?

What Do I Believe?

	Low				High

1. How successful am I?   1   2   3   4   5

    I would be more successful if _____

2. How significant am I?   1   2   3   4   5

    I would be more significant if _____

3. How fulfilled am I?   1   2   3   4   5

    I would be more fulfilled if _____

4. How satisfied am I?   1   2   3   4   5

    I would be more satisfied if _____

5. How happy am I?   1   2   3   4   5

    I would be happier if _____

6. How much fun am I having?   1   2   3   4   5

    I would have more fun if _____

7. How secure am I?   1   2   3   4   5

    I would be more secure if _____

8. How peaceful am I?   1   2   3   4   5

    I would have more peace if _____

Session 13
Staying On The Right Path

Focus Verse

Philippians 4:11-13: I am not saying this because I am in need, for I have learned to be content whatever the circumstances. I know what it is to be in need, and I know what it is to have plenty. I have learned the secret of being content in any and every situation, whether well fed or hungry, whether living in plenty or in want. I can do everything through him who gives me strength.

Objective

To help participants evaluate what they believe in the light of God's Word and make adjustments where necessary, so that they can stay on the path of becoming more like Jesus.

Focus Truth

If we want to be truly successful, fulfilled, satisfied, etc. we need to uncover and throw out false beliefs about what those things mean and commit ourselves to believing the truth in the Bible.

Welcome

Has anyone ever deceived you into believing something that turned out to be untrue?

Worship

Suggested theme: "His love endures for ever". See Psalm 100; 1 Chronicles 16:34; Jeremiah 33:10,11.

Word

Success Comes From Having The Right Goals

God's goal for your life begins with who you are on the basis of what God has already done for you (See 2 Peter 1:3-10).

We start with what we believe (faith). Our primary job then is diligently to adopt God's character goals — goodness (moral excellence), knowledge, self-control, perseverance, godliness, brotherly kindness and Christian love — and apply them to our lives. Focusing on God's goals will lead to success in God's terms.

Reaching God's goals is not dependent on other people or talents, intelligence or gifts. Every Christian can know who they are in Christ and grow in character.

For Joshua, success hinged entirely on one thing: whether or not he lived according to what God had said (Joshua 1:7,8).

Success is accepting God's goal for our lives and by His grace becoming what He has called us to be.

Significance Comes From Proper Use Of Time

What is forgotten in time is of little significance. What is remembered for eternity is of great significance.

"If any man's work... remains, he shall receive a reward." (1 Corinthians 3:14, NASB)

"Train yourself to be godly. For physical training is of some value, but godliness has value for all things, holding promise for both the present life and the life to come." (1 Timothy 4:7,8)

If you want to increase your significance, focus your energies on significant activities: those that will remain for eternity.

Fulfilment Comes From Serving Others

"Each one should use whatever gift he has received to serve others, faithfully administering God's grace in its various forms." (1 Peter 4:10)

Fulfilment is discovering our own uniqueness in Christ and using our gifts and talents to build others up and glorify the Lord.

The key is to discover the roles we occupy in which we cannot be replaced, and then decide to be the person God wants us to be in those roles.

Satisfaction Comes From Living A Quality Life

Satisfaction comes from living righteously and seeking to raise the level of quality in our relationships and in what we do.

"Blessed are those who hunger and thirst for righteousness, for they shall be filled." (Matthew 5:6)

Satisfaction is a quality issue, not a quantity issue. The key to personal satisfaction is not found in doing more things but in deepening our commitment to quality in the things that we are already doing.

Happiness Comes From Wanting What We Have

The world's concept of happiness is having what we want. Yet true happiness is wanting what we have.

"Godliness with contentment is great gain. For we brought nothing into the world, and we can take nothing out of it. But if we have food and clothing, we will be content with that." (1 Timothy 6:6-8)

If we focus on what we don't have, we'll be unhappy. If we begin to appreciate what we already have, we'll be happy all our lives.

Fun Comes From Enjoying Life Moment By Moment

Fun comes from throwing off inhibitions and being spontaneous. The secret is to remove unbiblical hindrances such as keeping up appearances.

It is a lot more fun pleasing the Lord than trying to please people.

Security Comes From Focusing On Eternal Values

We feel insecure when we depend upon earthly things that we have no right or ability to control. We can only find real security in the eternal life of Christ.

Jesus said no one can snatch us out of His hand (John 10:27-29).

Paul declared that nothing can separate us from the love of God in Christ (Romans 8:35-39) and that we are sealed "in Him" by the Holy Spirit (Ephesians 1:13,14).

"He is no fool to give up that which he cannot keep in order to gain that which he cannot lose." Jim Elliot

Peace Comes From Quieting The Inner Storm

Nobody can guarantee external peace because nobody can control people or circumstances.

The peace of God is internal, not external.

Peace *with* God is something we already have (Romans 5:1).
The peace *of* God is something we need to take hold of every day in our inner person. We can have the internal peace of God even in the midst of storms that rage in the external world.

"My peace I give you. I do not give to you as the world gives. Do not let your hearts be troubled and do not be afraid." (John 14:27)

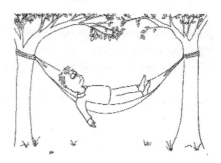

It's The First Day Of The Rest Of Your Life

Walking by faith comes down to making a decision every day to believe what God says is true and living accordingly by the power of the Holy Spirit.

Truth sets us free and we are transformed by the renewing of our minds.

Nothing and no one can prevent you from becoming the person God wants you to be — it hinges solely on your decision to adopt God's goal for your life.

I am part of the "Fellowship of the unashamed". I have Holy Spirit Power. The die has been cast. I've stepped over the line. The decision has been made. I am a disciple of His. I won't look back, let up, slow down, back away, or be still. My past is redeemed, my present makes sense, and my future is secure. I am finished and done with low-living, sight-walking, small-planning, smooth knees, colourless dreams, tame visions, mundane talking, miserly giving, and dwarfed goals!

I no longer need pre-eminence, prosperity, position, promotions, plaudits, or popularity. I don't have to be right, first, top, recognised, praised, regarded or rewarded. I now live by presence, lean by faith, love by patience, lift by prayer and labour by power.

My face is set, my gait is fast, my goal is heaven, my road is narrow, my way is rough, my companions few, my guide reliable, my mission clear. I cannot be bought, compromised, detoured, lured away, turned back, diluted or delayed. I will not flinch in the face of sacrifice, hesitate in the presence of adversity, negotiate at the table of the enemy, ponder at the pool of popularity, or meander in the maze of mediocrity.

I won't give up, shut up, let up or burn up till I've preached up, prayed up, paid up, stored up and stayed up for the cause of Christ.

I am a disciple of Jesus. I must go till He comes, give till I drop, preach till all know, and work till He stops.

And when He comes to get His own, He'll have no problems recognising me. My colours will be clear.

Witness:

How can adopting God's goal for your life affect your non-Christian friends?

Questions For Groups:

1. Do you believe that you can be a successful politician, business person, scientist, etc. and live consistently with God's Word? Why or why not?

2. What does our success as Christians depend upon?

3. What does the world call significant, that in the light of eternity is insignificant?

4. How can you live a more fulfilled life?

5. Can anything the flesh craves ever be satisfied? What satisfies and continues to satisfy?

6. How can you truly be happy in this world?

7. Fun may be fleeting, but the joy of the Lord lasts forever. How can you experience the joy of the Lord and make your Christian experience more fun?

8. What causes you to feel insecure? How can you be more secure?

9. How do goals and desires relate to the possibility of experiencing peace? What kind of peace can you have, and how do you get it?

To Take Away

Suggestions For Your Quiet Times This Week:

Work out which of the eight areas in the What Do I Believe? questionnaire are the most challenging for you. Spend some time reading the relevant passages for those areas in "God's Guidelines for the Walk of Faith" on page 112 (overleaf). You could use them to develop a Stronghold-Buster for the ongoing renewing of your mind.

God's Guidelines For The Walk Of Faith

Success comes from having the right goals
Success is accepting God's goal for our lives and by His grace becoming what He has called us to be (Joshua 1:7,8; 2 Peter 1:3-10; 3 John 2).

Significance comes from proper use of time
What is forgotten in time is of little significance. What is remembered for eternity is of greatest significance (1 Corinthians 3:13; Acts 5:33-40; 1 Timothy 4:7,8).

Fulfilment comes from serving others
Fulfilment is discovering our own uniqueness in Christ and using our gifts to build others up and glorify the Lord (2 Timothy 4:5; Romans 12:1-18; Matthew 25:14-30).

Satisfaction comes from living a quality life
Satisfaction is living righteously and seeking to raise the quality of our relationships and the things we do (Matthew 5:5; Proverbs 18:24; 2 Timothy 4:7).

Happiness comes from wanting what we have
Happiness is being thankful for what we do have, rather than focusing on what we don't have — because happy are the people who want what they have! (Philippians 4:12; 1 Thessalonians 5:18; 1 Timothy 6:6-8).

Fun comes from enjoying life moment by moment
The secret is to remove unbiblical hindrances such as keeping up appearances (2 Samuel 6:20-23; Galatians 1:10, 5:1; Romans 14:22).

Security comes from focusing on eternal values
Insecurity comes when we depend on things that will pass away rather than things that will last for ever (John 10:27-30; Romans 8:31-39; Ephesians 1:13,14).

Peace comes from quieting the inner storm
The peace of God is internal, not external (Jeremiah 6:14; John 14:27; Philippians 4:6,7; Isaiah 32:17).